THE LOVE ONE ANOTHER BIBLE STUDY SERIES

UNDERSTANDING
APPROACHING THINGS FROM ANOTHER'S POINT OF VIEW

A Bible Study by

Churches Alive!

MINISTERING TO THE CHURCHES OF THE WORLD
600 Meridian Avenue, Suite 200
San Jose, California 95126-3427

Published by

BRINGING TRUTH TO LIFE
NavPress Publishing Group
P.O. Box 35001, Colorado Springs, Colorado 80935

Cover photograph: Willard Clay
Interior cartoons: Bob Fuller

Printed in the United States of America

*Because we share kindred aims for helping local churches fulfill Christ's Great
Commission to "go and make disciples," NavPress and Churches Alive have
joined efforts on certain strategic publishing projects that are intended to bring
effective disciplemaking resources into the service of the local church.*

*For more than a decade, Churches Alive has teamed up with churches of all
denominations to establish vigorous disciplemaking ministries. At the same time,
NavPress has focused on publishing Bible studies, books, and other resources
that have grown out of The Navigators' 50 years of disciplemaking experience.*

*Now, together, we're working to offer special products like this one that are
designed to stimulate a deeper, more fruitful commitment to Christ in the local
gatherings of His Church.*

The LOVE ONE ANOTHER *series was written by Russ Korth, Ron Wormser, Jr., and
Ron Wormser, Sr. of Churches Alive. Many individuals from both Churches
Alive and NavPress contributed greatly in bringing this project to publication.*

Contents

Understanding is not a process of looking into someone else's head or psychoanalyzing him. God has given you some practical ways to increase your understanding of others.

Keys to Understanding

▼

1 a. List one subject you passed in school but never felt that you understood.

b. How do you feel about that subject now?

c. How do your feelings about that subject compare to your feelings about people you don't understand?

2 Do you think you can "pass" in your relationship to a person without understanding that person? Explain.

3 What is a basic principle of understanding? (Proverbs 28:5)

4 What are some things you can do to apply this principle of understanding?

5 How does the psalmist describe his experience of seeking the Lord and gaining understanding of certain people? (Psalm 73:12,16-18)

6 In what way does Proverbs 3:5-6 relate to seeking the Lord?

7 What are some ways to increase your understanding?

Psalm 111:10

Psalm 119:104

8 a. What is a basic tool that is used to enable us to understand one another? (Genesis 11:1-9)

b. How successful can this tool be? (Verse 6)

9 What precautions must you take in using this tool? (Proverbs 18:13,17)

10 Complete the following sentences:

In light of my present experience and needs, the most important thing I learned about gaining understanding is . . .

I plan to apply this by . . .

11 Complete the chart below

EVIDENCES OF UNDERSTANDING
Proverbs 11:12
Proverbs 12:11
Proverbs 14:29
Proverbs 17:27-28
Proverbs 20:5
Proverbs 28:16 (KJV—"wanteth" = "lacks")

12 a. Name an action that you listed in question 11 that needs improvement in your life.

b. How could a good understanding of others help to produce this action?

c. What can you do to improve in this area of your life?

13 Why is a good understanding of one another important to the well-being of your church?

14 What lessons regarding understanding are illustrated in the life of Solomon in 1 Kings 3:3-13?

LESSON TWO
Empathy

▼

1 Using a dictionary or other reference material, define "empathy."

2 Describe an emotional state in which you desire someone to express concern and empathy.

3 Read 1 Corinthians 2:11. How do you define "man's spirit" as used in this verse?

4 Why can we identify with most people? (1 Corinthians 10:13; KJV—"suffer" = "allow")

5 Write down your very specific paraphrase of Romans 12:15.

6 Hebrews 2:11 states that Jesus' identity with us means He is not ashamed to call us His brothers. If there ever was a time in your life when someone close to you was ashamed of you, describe how you felt. How does the knowledge that Jesus is never ashamed of you make you feel?

7 How do you think the truth of Proverbs 21:2 relates to your desire to have others empathize with you?

8 How is empathy expressed in Hebrews 13:3?

9 a. What has enabled Jesus to understand and empathize with you? (Hebrews 2:17-18, 4:15-16)

b. How does this affect your relationship with Him?

10 a. Read John 8:1-11. Do you think Jesus was empathiz-
ing with the woman? Explain.

b. In what ways can you identify with the woman?

Differences are useful in identifying each person in a
group photograph. But there are more important reasons
God has created you with great individuality.

Recognizing Differences

1 What are some ways people are obviously different from one another?

2 a. In what ways do you enjoy being different from others?

b. In what ways do you not enjoy being different?

3 What are three important differences that exist among believers? (1 Corinthians 12:4-6)

4 Hebrews 11 lists many different effects of living by faith. List at least five pleasant and five unpleasant (yet profitable) results of faith from Hebrews 11:32-38.

PLEASANT RESULTS	UNPLEASANT RESULTS

5 A Christian whose family was plagued by adversity was told that if he had more faith, his life would not be so difficult. Does the passage in Hebrews 11 support this statement? Why, or why not?

6 a. How did Jesus describe the difference between His lifestyle and that of John the Baptist? (Luke 7:31-34; KJV—"winebibber" = "drunkard")

b. In your opinion, why did the Pharisees and lawyers reject both of them?

7 In light of these differences, what do you think Luke 7:35 means?

8 What important lesson did Jesus teach about God's plans for different people in John 21:18-22?

9 What wrong reactions did the Corinthians have when recognizing differences? (1 Corinthians 1:11-12, 3:3-7)

10 a. What practice are you warned against in 2 Corinthians 10:12?

b. In your opinion, why is this practice unwise?

11 It has been said that many people spend their lives attempting to take God's role and recreate others in their own image.

a. When people make this attempt, what truths about differences do you think they are ignoring?

b. How would a better understanding help displace this tendency?

Accepting Differences

▼

1 Describe a situation while you were growing up in which you were not accepted for being different.

2 a. Read 1 Corinthians 3:3-9. How was the lack of acceptance of differences expressed by the Corinthians?

b. What is one similar situation that occurs today?

c. How can you follow the example of Paul in accepting others?

3 For each of the following sentences, choose the ending that best describes your actions (not attitudes). There are no right or wrong, good or bad answers.

MY MANNER OF BEHAVIOR		
Other people interpret this behavior in positive or in negative terms. Some interpretations may be:		
	Positive	**Negative**
I usually—		
☐ show my feelings.	Friendly, caring	Flighty, emotional
☐ do not show my feelings.	Serious, calm	Uncaring, a loner
When speaking, I tend to—		
☐ make statements.	Confident, stable	Dogmatic, proud
☐ ask questions.	Supportive, appreciative of others' ideas	Unsure, wishy-washy
I would generally prefer discussing—		
☐ personal feelings and day-to-day experiences.	People-centered, interested in them	Egotistic, naive
☐ facts, ideas, and concepts.	Intelligent, objective	Insensitive, insecure

If you are married, set a time to spend thirty minutes to discuss your responses to question 3 with your spouse. The objective of your discussion is to better understand one another.

Our appointment to discuss this is . . .

Day: *Time:*

4 Why would changing any of your responses to question 3 not make you more pleasing to God?

5 a. According to Romans 15:5-7, how should you relate to others?

b. How is this possible in view of the many differences there are among people?

6 Why should we accept others the way they are? (Romans 14:1,3; KJV—"doubtful disputations" = "judge his opinions")

7 What is the difference between accepting a person and condoning his activities?

8 Why do you think accepting one another is important in fulfilling James 5:16? (KJV—"availeth" = "accomplishes")

9 What are some areas in which you want others to accept your differences?

10 Identify someone to whom you should express acceptance.

a. What can you do that will help this person sense your acceptance?

b. When do you plan to do this?

If you remain stiff and unbending, you force others to
accommodate you. If you attempt to adapt to everyone else,
you end up compromising. Good understanding will
enable you to accommodate others properly.

Accommodating Others

▼

1 a. What attitude is necessary if you are to accommodate others? (Philippians 2:3-4)

b. How was this attitude demonstrated by God? (Philippians 2:5-8)

2 What reasons for accommodating others do you see in Romans 15:1-3?

3 Why should you adapt your actions to suit others?
(1 Corinthians 8:13)

4 What are some ways Paul accommodated nonbelievers?
(1 Corinthians 9:19-23) Explain.

5 In what way did Peter and John refuse to accommodate nonbelievers? (Acts 4:18-22)

6 What are some ways that you can adapt the gospel message
to the needs of people without compromising the truth?

7 a. What was Paul's evaluation of circumcision? (Galatians 5:6)

b. What did Paul do at Lystra? (Acts 16:1-3)

c. Why do you think he did this?

8 What was wrong with Peter's (Cephas') action in Antioch? (Galatians 2:11-16)

9 What do you think is the difference between accommodating others and pleasing men as mentioned in Galatians 1:10?

10 a. Make a list of at least three specific ways you can accommodate people in your church.

   b. List at least three specific ways you should not accommodate others in your church.

It is far easier to find fault with others than to understand them. Fault-finding is wrong even when your evaluation is accurate. True understanding will enable you to judge in the correct way.

Being Critical

▼

The concept of "being critical" is used in this section in the negative sense of finding fault and condemning.

1 What is a name or expression that is used to describe people who are critical of others? Why is this name or expression used?

2 Why should you not be critical of others? (Matthew 7:1-5, James 4:11-12; KJV—"mote" = "speck")

3 What does Romans 2:1-2 say about you when you are critical of others?

4 What would have kept the Pharisees from being critical of the disciples in Matthew 12:1-7?

5 What is a mistake people often make in evaluating others? (2 Corinthians 10:12)

6 a. On what basis was Nathaniel initially negative about Jesus? (John 1:43-57)

b. Why were the disciples critical of others? (Mark 9:38-41)

c. What are some current parallels to these situations?

7 Review questions 2-5 and complete this sentence: *Being critical of others shows a lack of understanding because* . . .

8 What are some of the ways a critical attitude toward others may be expressed?

9 Why is it so hard to evaluate people correctly? (Proverbs 14:13)

10 What mistake do people usually make? (1 Samuel 16:7)

11 Rewrite John 7:24 to express how you want others to evaluate you in a specific area of life.

12 Rewrite John 7:24 to express how you plan to evaluate a specific person in a specific area of life.

Discernment

▼

1 Describe a situation when you observed someone demonstrate unusual discernment.

2 What is necessary to have accurate judgment? (John 8:15-16)

3 Consider 1 Corinthians 2:9-16 and complete the following sentences:

Verse 9—*Spiritual insight is not gained by . . .*

Verse 10—*Spiritual insight is gained by . . .*

Verses 11-12—*We are equipped to gain insight by . . .*

Verses 15-16—*The key to discernment is . . .*

4 Read 1 Corinthians 4:5.

a. What is the Lord going to do after His return which will assure righteous judgment?

b. What implications does this have for you today?

5 How can you follow Jesus' example in making accurate judgments? (John 5:30)

6 List the characteristics of human-based discernment and God-sent discernment. (James 3:13-18; KJV—"conversation" = "way of life," "easy to be entreated" = "willing to yield")

HUMAN-BASED DISCERNMENT	GOD-SENT DISCERNMENT

7 On what basis did Jesus suggest we should make evaluations of others? (Matthew 7:15-20)

8 What will equip you to evaluate what is right? (Hebrews 5:13-14)

9 When you've discerned a problem in another believer, what is the proper attitude and the proper action for you to take? (Galatians 6:1)

10 What did you learn in this chapter about practical ways judging (using discernment) can be beneficial to your church?

11 What are some practical safeguards that can help you maintain good discernment as studied in this lesson and not become critical as studied in the previous lesson?

When there is an honest difference of opinion, many people would rather fight about it than understand the other viewpoint. The Scriptures clearly establish many areas of Christian behavior, but there are other areas where the Bible is silent or not conclusive. This leads to honest differences of opinion.

Understanding Others' Convictions

▼

1 It has been said that there are dog lovers and there are cat lovers. What do you think would help these two kinds of people understand each other better?

2 What were subjects of controversy that Paul wrote about?

Romans 14:2,5

1 Corinthians 8:4,7-8

In each of these issues there were those who felt an activity,
such as eating meat, was acceptable behavior and those who
felt it was not. For purposes of communication in this study,
these two groups will be referred to as "partakers" and "nonpartakers." Note that "partakers" consider an activity acceptable
but that they may or may not actually be practicing this activity.

3 What are some current issues that have "partakers" and
"nonpartakers"?

4 What basic attitude should a "partaker" have toward a
"nonpartaker"? (Romans 14:3)

5 What is the view a "partaker" might have of a "nonpartaker" which would make it difficult for him to maintain the
attitude mentioned in question 4?

6 What basic attitude should a "nonpartaker" have toward a "partaker"? (Romans 14:3-4)

7 What is the view a "nonpartaker" might have of a "partaker" which would make it difficult for him to maintain the attitude mentioned in question 6?

8 Choose one of the following passages: Romans 14, 1 Corinthians 8, 1 Corinthians 10:19-33. Identify other proper attitudes and list them in the appropriate column. (If something applies to both, list it in both columns.)

ATTITUDES FOR A PARTAKER	ATTITUDES FOR A NONPARTAKER

9 Complete the following sentences, using one of the topics you mentioned in your answer to question 3 or another topic of your own choosing:

Because I am a "nonpartaker" in the practice of
_____ *I must guard*

against a judgmental attitude.

Because I am a "partaker" in the practice of
_____ *I must guard*

against a contemptuous attitude.

10 What do you think was Paul's reason for not telling the church at Rome if it was right to eat meat?

Sensitivity to Others' Convictions

▼

1 In what ways do you want others to be sensitive to your ideas?

2 In the chart make a list of five things commonly practiced today that the Bible clearly states are wrong. Next to each wrong practice list a Bible reference which shows that the practice is wrong. (You may find 1 Corinthians 6:8-10 and Galatians 5:19-21 helpful. KJV—"expedient" = "profitable")

WRONG PRACTICES	REFERENCES
Drunkenness	*Ephesians 5:18*

3 In what ways do you think you should be sensitive to another believer whom you see commit one of the offenses listed in question 2?

4 Is every activity not prohibited in Scripture acceptable behavior for believers? Explain.

5 a. What was true about people on both sides of the issue in Romans 14:6-12?

b. Do you think the attitudes expressed in verse 6 about controversial areas of behavior are usually true of Christians? Explain your answer.

6 List the criteria you should use to determine whether an activity is right or wrong for you.

Romans 14:5,14

Romans 14:19,23

1 Corinthians 6:12

1 Corinthians 10:23,31

7 To be sensitive to others, what factors need to be considered in determining your behavior?

Romans 14:13-23

1 Corinthians 10:27-33

8 What can result from using your liberty unwisely? (1 Corinthians 8:10-12)

9 A friend from your Sunday school class in talking to you in private about a particular activity says, "I know it is not a sin to do it, but I feel awful just thinking about it." Later at a planning session for a Sunday school party someone suggests the same activity. What do you think is a sensitive way of handling this situation?

Notes and Prayer Requests

NOTES AND PRAYER REQUESTS

If you enjoyed this study, you'll want to check out the other titles in the LOVE ONE ANOTHER series:

SMALL-GROUP MATERIALS FROM NAVPRESS

BIBLE STUDY SERIES

CRISISPOINTS FOR WOMEN
DESIGN FOR DISCIPLESHIP
GOD IN YOU
GOD'S DESIGN FOR THE FAMILY
INSTITUTE OF BIBLICAL
   COUNSELING SERIES

LIFECHANGE
LIFESTYLE SMALL GROUP SERIES
LOVE ONE ANOTHER
STUDIES IN CHRISTIAN LIVING
THINKING THROUGH DISCIPLESHIP

TOPICAL BIBLE STUDIES

Becoming a Woman of
   Excellence
Becoming a Woman of Freedom
The Blessing Study Guide
Celebrating Life
Growing in Christ
Growing Strong in God's Family
Homemaking
Intimacy with God

Loving Your Husband
Loving Your Wife
A Mother's Legacy
Surviving Life in the Fast Lane
To Run and Not Grow Tired
To Walk and Not Grow Weary
What God Does When Men Pray
When the Squeeze Is On

BIBLE STUDIES WITH COMPANION BOOKS

Bold Love
From Bondage to Bonding
Hiding from Love
Inside Out
The Masculine Journey
The Practice of Godliness
The Pursuit of Holiness

Secret Longings of the
   Heart
Transforming Grace
Trusting God
What Makes a Man?
The Wounded Heart
Your Work Matters to God

RESOURCES

Curriculum Resource Guide
How to Lead Small Groups
Jesus Cares for Women
The Small Group Leaders
   Training Course

Topical Memory System (KJV/NIV
   and NASB/NKJV)
Topical Memory System: Life
   Issues (KJV/NIV and
   NASB/NKJV)

VIDEO PACKAGES

Abortion
Bold Love
Hope Has Its Reasons
Inside Out

Living Proof
Parenting Adolescents
Unlocking Your Sixth Suitcase
Your Home, A Lighthouse

Churches Alive!

This study is just one item in a wide range of small group material authored by Churches Alive. Continue your study with other books in this series.

Churches Alive has local representatives who provide their own living expenses to serve you at your church. On-site support and training conferences will develop commitment and vision in group leaders. Our experienced staff can help you develop leaders, enrich your groups, and reach out to others.

Conferences and Support Services

A Pastor's Perspective:

"Churches Alive was a tremendous help to us when we were getting started in our discipleship ministry. We had to make a choice—either try to learn ourselves and make a lot of mistakes, or get some help and minimize mistakes. Their careful but goal-oriented approach helps any church build a solid, perpetuating ministry."

Churches Alive!
600 Meridian Avenue
Suite 200
San Jose, CA 95126
(408) 294-6000
(408) 294-6029 FAX

Conferences

Designed to strengthen the effectiveness of your leaders, our conferences and seminars range from one to four days. Most are taught by Churches Alive staff and local pastors. In addition, we arrange special seminars in your church to encourage people in your church to study the Bible.

Support Services

In dozens of denominations, our staff helps churches large and small. We can help you evaluate, plan, train leaders, and expand your small groups. Invite a Churches Alive representative to explore small group discipleship at your church.

Call 1-800-755-3787